SOUTH POLAR TIMES

SUPER SAN

A David Bennett Book

First published in 1991 by
Kingfisher Books,
Grisewood & Dempsey Ltd,
Elsley House,
24-30 Great Titchfield Street,
London W1P 7AD

Text copyright © 1991
Annie Civardi
Illustrations copyright © 1991
Clive Scruton

BRITISH LIBRARY CATALOGUING IN PUBLICATION DATA
Civardi, Anne
The secrets of Santa ho ho ho!
I. Title II. Scruton, Clive
823.914 [J]
ISBN 0 86272 675 1

Created and produced by
David Bennett Books Ltd,
94 Victoria Street, St Albans,
Herts, AL1 3TG

Typesetting by Type City
Production by Imago
Printed in Singapore

PEREGRINE PENGUIN TO DISCOVER THE SECRETS OF SANTA

Never before in the history of Icy Land has a penguin visited the North Pole. But, late last night, from his throne in Iceberg Castle, the Emperor Penguin made an important announcement.

A letter has arrived from Santa inviting Peregrine Penguin, our brilliant chief waddling reporter, to Santa City.

Peregrine, who was named Writer of the Year in a glittering ceremony last week, will be the first penguin ever to discover the amazing secrets of Santa.

Every week until Christmas, in his own special Santa Supplement, Peregrine will send us back his Super Santa Story.

Good luck, Peregrine Penguin.

THE SECRETS OF SANTA

as told to
ANNIE CIVARDI

Illustrated by
CLIVE SCRUTON

*For Todd, Sophie, Jake
and Amber*
A. C.

*For Ben and Hannah's
Grandpa, with love*
C. S.

Kingfisher Books

I'm Peregrine Penguin, chief waddling reporter for the South Polar Times. As you've most probably read, I'm about to go to Santa City. Fancy Santa choosing *me* to tell the world about his secrets. Yeeks, what a fantastic scoop.

I've just said goodbye to the Emperor Penguin and I've promised not to leave a snowball unturned. I won't let him down. I'm going to find out *everything* about Santa.

My bags are packed and I'm ready to go. Yep, I've got everything a good reporter needs - my trusty old tape recorder, my note pad and my camera.

It's a long way to Santa City...

through the steamy jungle...

over the high mountain peaks...

across the burning desert...

and around the crowded cities.

At last I've arrived!

As soon as I arrived at the North Pole, Sid the Snowman drove me straight here to Santa City. It's the most glittering place I've ever seen.

Who would have guessed it? Santa lives in a glimmering white palace with his assistant, a polar bear called Gloria, and six little elves - Robin, Holly, Ivy, Carol, Noel and Nicholas.

One of the elves has just let me in. Oops! I think I'm a bit early. Santa's still in bed having his breakfast.

Yeeks! I can't believe that's really him. He's just as jolly and rosy and round as I'd always imagined. Just think, I'm about to meet him and find out all his secrets.

Hello, young Peregrine.

How do you do, Santa?

Morning, Ivy!

Nice work, Holly.

You've got a busy day!

Santa is stopping at the Ice Port first. He passes it every morning on his way to work in the Santa City Post Office. Yeeks, it's a noisy place!

All night long, his special delivery planes have been landing on the runway. They're packed with letters from children.

Lots of big strong snowmen are hurrying to unload the huge sacks of mail. They're working so hard, they're almost melting.

Flapping flippers! There's another plane circling around the Ice Port. Poor Santa, he's got a lot of reading to do today. We'd better hurry to the Post Office.

This must be the busiest Post Office in the world. The elves in the sorting room are opening the letters for Santa to read. Whopping whales! What a job! Icy Land doesn't get this many letters in a whole year.

When Santa's read all the letters and made all the toys the children want this year, the snowmen store them in a special room. Santa never *ever* throws a single letter away.

Santa's just finished reading today's batch of mail. A little girl has asked him for a flying penguin. Can you believe it? She wants a toy like me.

Now we're in Santa's Playroom checking his special penguin cupboard. Nope, he hasn't got any flying penguins. He'll have to invent one.

Frozen fishcakes! Santa's so clever. His Playroom's full of toys he's already invented. I bet it won't take him long to make a flying penguin.

Whopping whales! Santa's worked hard on his flying penguin. And now that it's absolutely perfect, he's letting me into one of his biggest secrets of all.

Guess what? Santa has his own special top secret toy factory right in the middle of Santa City! Absolutely nobody's allowed in here without his permission.

Yeeks, I can't believe my eyes. This must be the most exciting place in the whole wide world. There are gigantic toy machines everywhere. Hundreds of elves and snowmen are hard at work, testing, checking and loading up the toys to take to Santa's warehouse. There's even a packing machine wrapping them up.

Flapping flippers! What's that over there? It's a enormous penguin machine and it's making hundreds of baby flying penguins. Yeeks, you're never going to believe this. I'll have to take a photograph and send it to Icy Land for my supplement.

Yeeks, I only just escaped in time to meet Santa and Gloria at Fred Well's shop. Fred's the finest tailor in Santa City. Every year, he makes Santa a special suit to wear on Christmas Eve. Hmm, I think Fred's got something up his sleeve for Santa today!

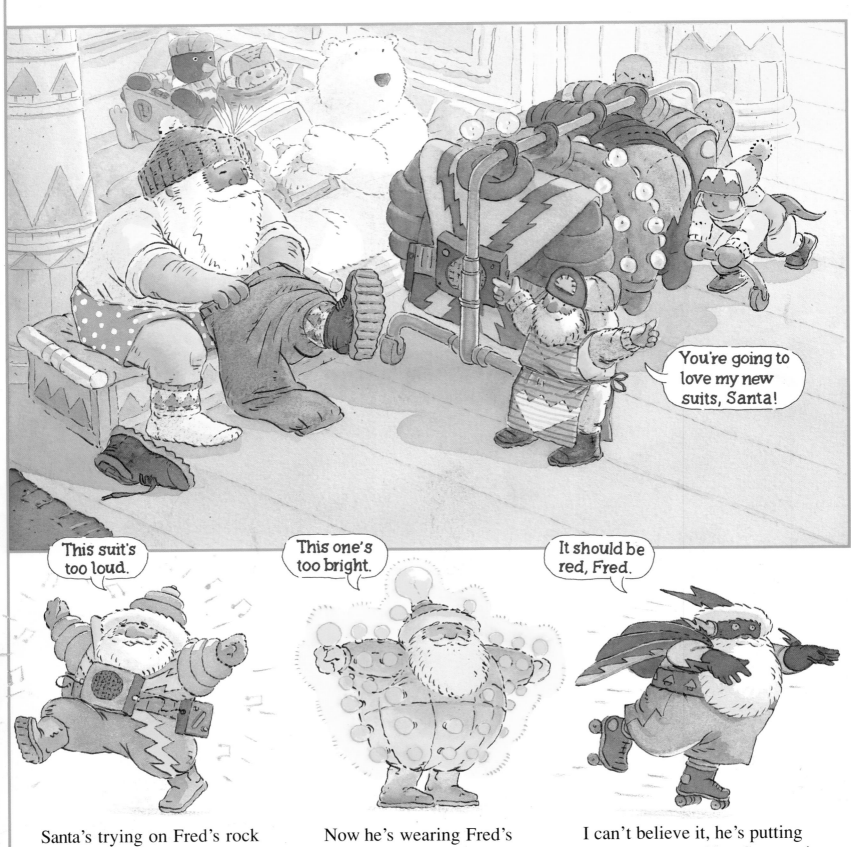

Santa's trying on Fred's rock and roll Santa suit first. Nope, it's not quite right.

Now he's wearing Fred's glitter and glow suit. Uh, hum, it's not right either.

I can't believe it, he's putting on Fred's super blue Santa suit. That certainly isn't right.

SANTA SU

REINDEER TRIALS DAY ON MISTLETOE MOUNTAIN

by waddling reporter Peregrine Penguin in Santa City

I t was a crisp and chilly morning, high above Santa City, when one of the most important events of the year took place here yesterday.

Sleigh bells rang all over the North Pole as hundreds of young flying reindeer gathered on Mistletoe Mountain to take part in the Reindeer Trials for a place in Santa's team.

For weeks, Santa's snowmen had been busy building the tricky course and stocking up the Neigh Bars with snacks for the hungry reindeer.

SANTA FOLLOWS RACE IN RED BALLOON

At exactly 10 o'clock, wrapped up warmly against the chilly wind, Santa arrived in his red balloon to start the race. Throngs of hopeful reindeer burst through the starting gate and flew off to the first huge hurdle - Chimney Slalom.

Far above them, floating across the clear blue sky, Santa watched the reindeer streak around the course. What a competition it was. Never had so many bold new reindeer raced together before.

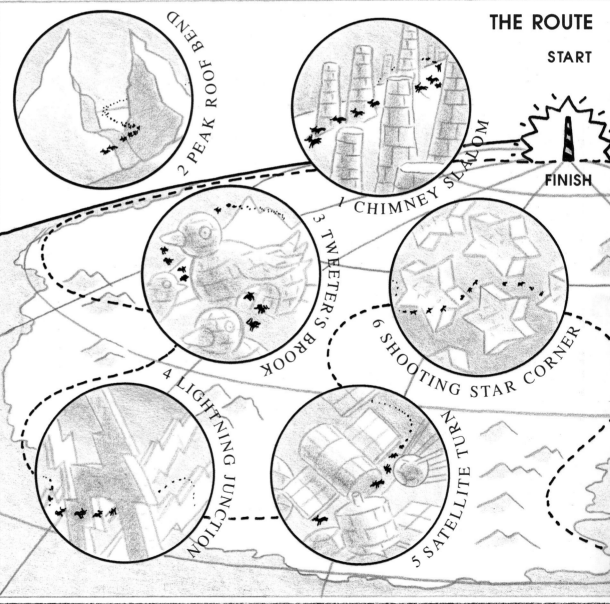

THE ROUTE

START

FINISH

1 CHIMNEY SLALOM

2 PEAK ROOF BEND

3 TWEETER'S BROOK

4 LIGHTNING JUNCTION

5 SATELLITE TURN

6 SHOOTING STAR CORNER

SNOWBALL STOPS PRANCER

It was one of the most difficult courses ever. Only the bravest and best new jumpers made it through Lightning Junction, past Hazard Mountain and through Thunder Pass, the most difficult obstacles in the entire race.

For three hours, Prancer, the favourite, led the way. Then suddenly, as he swooped past Thick Cloud Underpass to Snowball Station, a huge snowball struck him on the head and Ding Dong, Hosanna and Tinsel thundered past.

TINSEL AND DING DONG WIN PLACES ON SANTA'S TEAM

Finally, at the end of a brilliant race, the winners, Ding Dong and Tinsel, galloped past the finishing post.

There wasn't an inch between these two magnificent reindeer as they broke the winning tape to the delight of the onlookers.

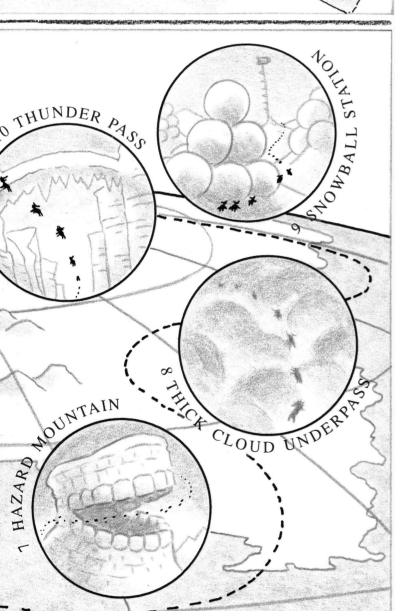

SANTA PRESENTS THE PRIZES

The snowmen roared and the elves cheered loudly as Santa presented the winners with their prizes - a special Christmas harness with a silver bell, which they will wear on the Big Night.

The Reindeer Trials have ended and the contestants have all gone home. But on Christmas Eve, these two brave new reindeer will be there, helping to pull Santa's sleigh.

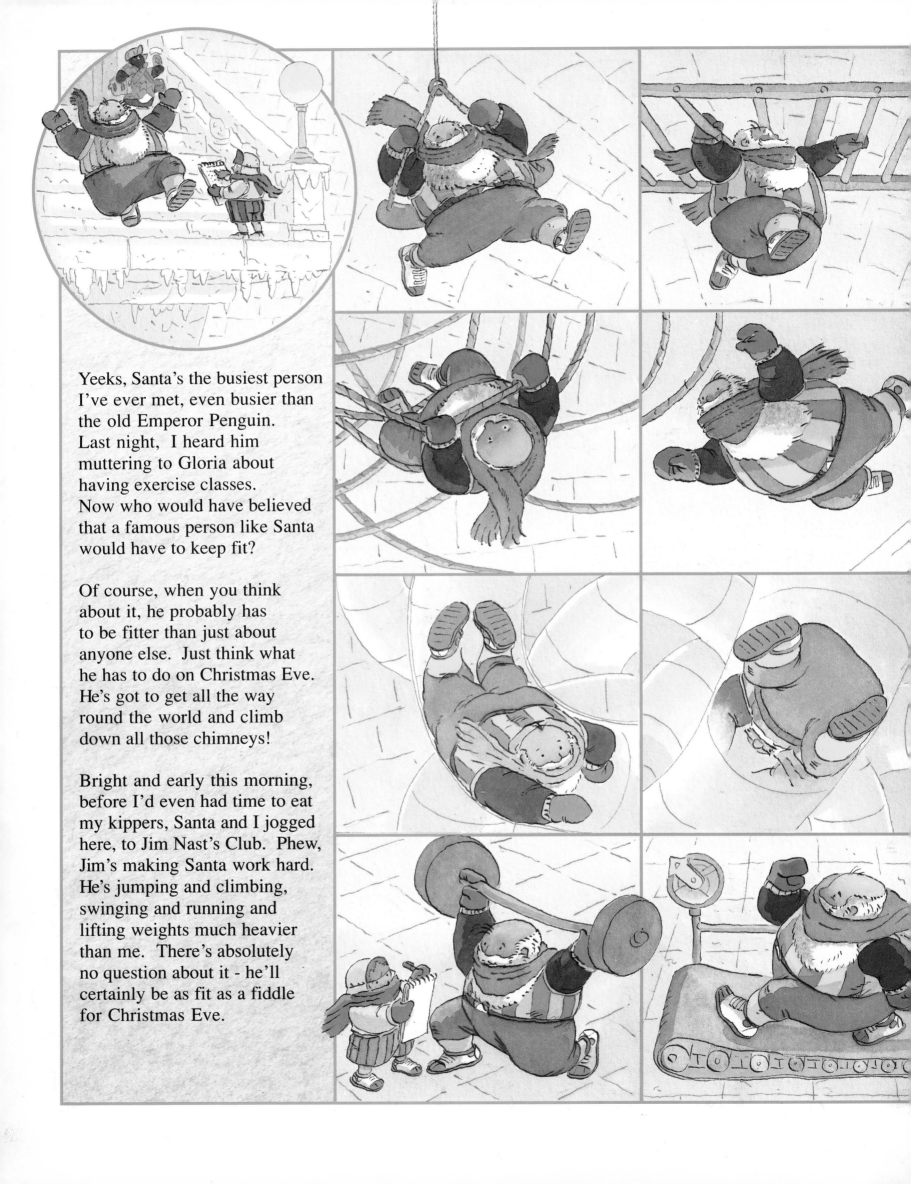

Yeeks, Santa's the busiest person I've ever met, even busier than the old Emperor Penguin. Last night, I heard him muttering to Gloria about having exercise classes. Now who would have believed that a famous person like Santa would have to keep fit?

Of course, when you think about it, he probably has to be fitter than just about anyone else. Just think what he has to do on Christmas Eve. He's got to get all the way round the world and climb down all those chimneys!

Bright and early this morning, before I'd even had time to eat my kippers, Santa and I jogged here, to Jim Nast's Club. Phew, Jim's making Santa work hard. He's jumping and climbing, swinging and running and lifting weights much heavier than me. There's absolutely no question about it - he'll certainly be as fit as a fiddle for Christmas Eve.

You'll never guess where we are now - the Santa City School.

Yep, there's actually a special school for Santa and the elves. Just what does someone like Santa need to learn, for goodness sake?

Ah, he's brushing up on his map reading with a clever elf called Irma Lost. Of course, he has to remember how to get to every single country in the world.

Now Ali Looyer's giving him a language lesson to make sure he can read all the signposts on the Big Night. Yeeks! I never realised how much Santa has to learn.

His next class is with jolly Miss L. Toe. She's reminding Santa how to tiptoe quietly so he won't wake any children when he's filling their stockings.

Oh dear, Tinsel and Ding Dong aren't doing very well in their sleigh lesson. Ding Dong can't remember his left from his right and he keeps bumping into things. I hope he does better on the Big Night.

It's Christmas Eve at last. And guess what, Santa's asked *me*, *yes, me*, Peregrine Penguin, to go with him on his sleigh. Yeeks, yippee, whopping whales, what an incredible scoop!

Before we set off, Santa's making his last minute rounds to check that everything's ready for the Big Night. We've just popped in to see the reindeer to make sure they've eaten all their supper. Phew, they're going to need lots of carrots tonight!

Next door, old Tom Boggan's giving Santa's sleigh a final inspection. Wow, what a magnificent flying machine!

Ho, ho, ho! I love Christmas so.

Hey, hey, hey! More presents for Santa's sleigh.

The Toy Factory's still buzzing with action. Those snowmen have been working day and night taking presents to the Sleigh Port. They're the hardest working snowmen I've ever seen. I hope they remember to pack some flying penguins!

Ho, ho, ho! It's time for Santa to get dressed.

You're late, Santa.

Good old Gloria. She's got a list of things that Santa needs.

Noel's giving Santa his favourite mince pies and some holly berry tea to send him on his way. He certainly won't get hungry tonight.

Don't forget Hawaii.

Do you know what? It takes five elves to dress Santa on Christmas Eve. I can't believe how many clothes he has to wear so he won't catch cold as he whizzes around the world.

So far, he's put on his new long johns, a thermal vest, three pairs of socks, two jerseys, a scarf, and two pairs of gloves. And here's a hot secret. I saw Santa slipping a big hot water bottle inside his long johns, right over his tummy! As for his new Santa suit, Fred Well's done a brilliant job.

Santa's almost ready - just his boots to go. Heave ho, Holly and Ivy. One, two, three, pull.

Okey, dokey. It's just about time for Santa to leave for the Sleigh Port. But first he's having a final run through the flight plan with Gloria. The route's been changed because there are strong winds blowing in from the east.

I'm dreaming dum de dum dum dum...

I wish you could see this. It's quite out of this world. I'm inside Santa's Sleigh Port, surrounded by hundreds of flashing lights, dials and computer screens.

What a tremendous night this is. The whole place is tingling with excitement as Santa and his reindeer get ready to take off.

Santa's helpers are working at a furious pace. Ah, here come more snowmen with even more presents. They'll have to hurry, the huge Sleigh Port doors are opening. It's time for Santa to go.

Wait for me, reindeer!

S-s-s-sorry, Frosty.

Watch out, Iceblockhead!

Before we set off, Noel's making sure that all the children are fast asleep.

Robin's checking the weather report. Santa will have to watch out for that east wind.

Holly and Ivy are giving the team of reindeer their final flying instructions.

Everything's ready as Carol guides Santa and the reindeer towards the doors.

Now Gloria's jumped out of the sleigh to shout out the final countdown.

Ho, ho, ho, it's time to go. Santa, *me* and the reindeer are off to fill stockings!

Yeeks, what a take-off. We're zooming across the sky faster than a rocket. This is the most exciting night of my life.

One minute we're up in the stars; the next we're diving down, down, down. I never realized before how big the world is. Just think of all the millions of children fast asleep in their beds, dreaming of what Santa might bring them.

You'll never believe the trouble Santa has getting into some of the houses. Sometimes the chimneys are too small and sometimes they're too big. Sometimes there isn't one at all. But Santa never *ever* gives up.

Once he's inside, Santa has all sorts of other problems, such as big fierce dogs, hungry cats and very prickly Christmas trees. Yeeks, what a job!

As if that wasn't enough, he sometimes hears children talking. Flapping flippers, they *must* know that Santa can't fill stockings until *everybody* is sound asleep.

Santa's only got one more stocking to fill up tonight. Do you know what? It belongs to the little girl who asked him for a flying penguin. Yeeks, what a grand surprise she'll get tomorrow morning.

Hurry up, Santa, it's time to fly back to Santa City.

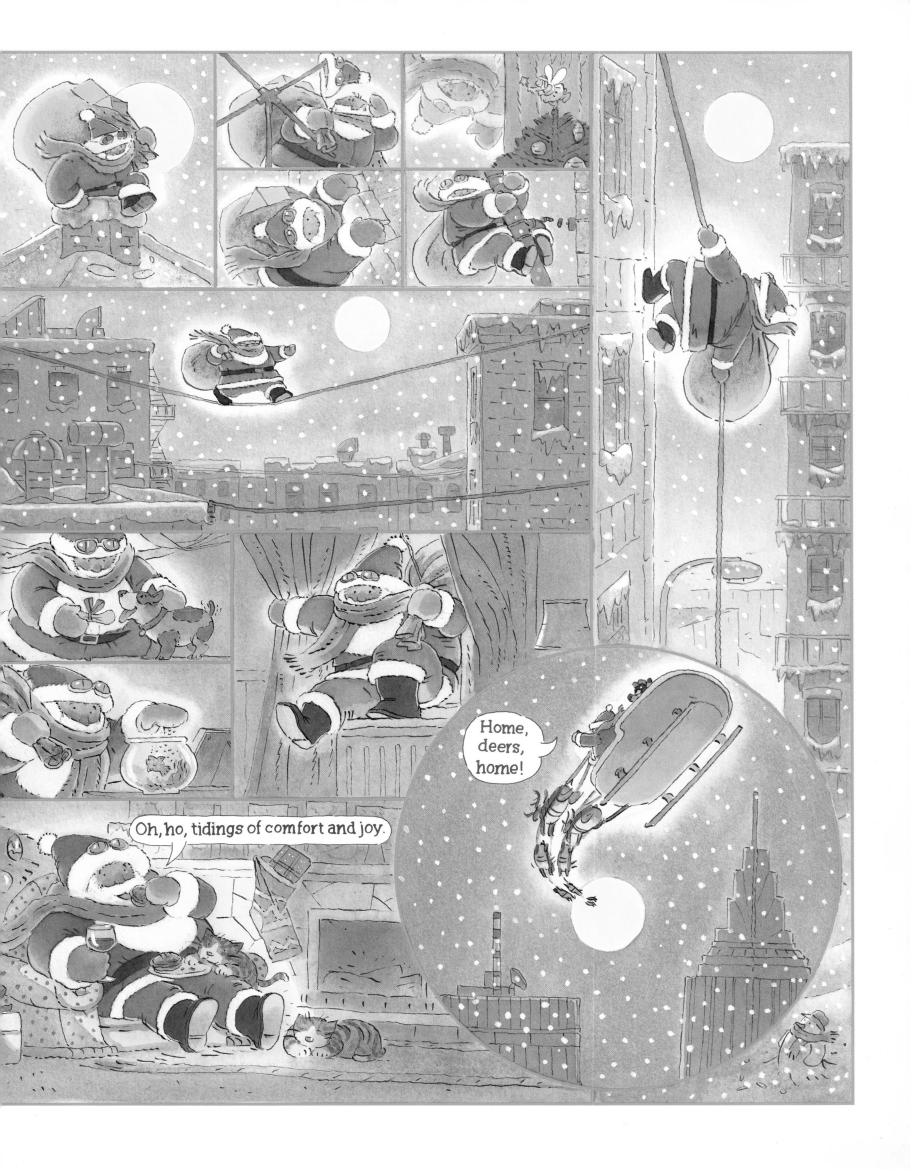

Yeeks, that was fast! We're already back in Santa City. I can see the Ice Palace sparkling in the darkness.

Absolutely everyone's come out to welcome us home. Santa's done it again, he's delivered all his presents without a hitch.

Of course, he couldn't have done it without the reindeer. They did an incredibly brilliant job tonight.

Ah, here comes Gloria. She's telling Santa to hurry up and get dressed for the Christmas party. I wonder what he's going to wear!

Three cheers for Santa!